Your Best You

A Woman's Guide & Journal

By Gayle Woodard

Special thanks—
Thank you to Beatrice Arbuckle and
Book Club Team Members

Scripture notations noted are quoted from Holy Bible New International Version and English Standard Version

First Printing Edition 2021

ISBN #: 978-0-578-85921-7

Your Best You

To: Tamron Hall

I love your show

"you are the best"

love you

Gayle Woodard

Greetings

Greetings my sister,

God has given me the vision to help many women from all walks of life. Knowing that as a woman, you are a beautiful flower, rooted, planted, and flourished by the hands of your heavenly father is essential to reaching Your Best You. Together we will use this guide as a spiritual mirror to see in ourselves what God already sees. Psalms 139:14 says, "I will praise you, for I am fearfully and wonderfully made; marvelous are your works, and that my soul knows very well." This women's guide can be explored by women's ministries, organizations, book clubs, and girl groups. As we study the word of God, a transformation will take place in each one of us.

Get ready! Let's discover Your Best You!

Your friend indeed,

Gayle Woodard

Affirmation

My best is knowing my worth, who my creator is, that I am fearfully and wonderfully made—that I am unique and different, that I am a royal priesthood, and that I am above rubies and diamonds. I am discovering the best in me and embracing that I am God 's masterpiece! I am exploring the best in me, knowing that it will be best for the world to see. I am bold, beautiful, smart, classy, sweet, kind, and focused. I know where I am going. I will do better, act better, live better, work better, and think better. I will continue to bring out the best in me. I was created to be my best self even with flaws and imperfections. I am anointed and appointed to carry out my purpose in my life. I am the best! Now it is time to start taking the steps toward living my best life!

"Write the vision; make it plain on tablets, so he may run who reads it. For still the vision awaits its appointed time; it hastens to the end- it will not lie. If it seems slow, wait for it; it will surely come; it will not delay."

—Habakkuk 2:2-3

ACTIVITY

**Break up into teams and take turns acting out a short skit
demonstrating each category below.**

Your Best Attire

Your Best Creativity

Your Best Career

Your Best Character

Your Best Faith

Notes

Notes

Notes

Do You Know Who You Are?

"Yet to all who did receive him, to those who believed in his name, he gave the right to become children of God."
John 1:12

Have you taken the first step to receive him? Why or why not?

_____

_____

_____

_____

_____

What do you think when you see yourself in the mirror?

_____

_____

_____

_____

_____

How does God fit into your lifestyle?

_____

_____

_____

_____

_____

How has this right to become a child of God empowered your confidence?

_____
_____
_____
_____
_____

How can you improve being sure and knowing who you are?

_____
_____
_____
_____
_____

"Many receive advice, only the wise profit from it."
—Harper Lee

What is Your Value?

**"I praise you, for I am fearfully and wonderfully made.
Wonderful are your works; my soul knows it very well."**
Psalm 139:14

What makes you feel valued?

_____
_____
_____
_____
_____

Do you know your value and if so, how do you know it?

_____
_____
_____
_____
_____

In what ways do your family, spouse, or friends value you?

_____
_____
_____
_____
_____

If God created you all over again, what would you want him to change or add?

_____

_____

_____

_____

_____

If God made those changes, would you be able to fulfill your purpose?

_____

_____

_____

_____

_____

"There is no greater gift you can give or receive than to honor your calling. It's why you were born."
—Oprah Winfrey

Does Your Character Shine?

I choose to be an example of a woman with a character that exemplifies, honor, beauty, and love. I am the daughter of the most high. I will take pride in my character as I help others to shine their character in this world. My character shines like a bright light. My character will take me places further than my ability can. With great character, I can change a negative environment into a positive one. Maya Angelou said, "People may not remember exactly what you did or said, but they will always remember how you made them feel." My character will speak volumes not only in my home, but in my place of worship, my place of work and among my family and friends. Good character can last in a memory for a lifetime.

I want people to remember my character as
_____ and _____.

Choose 2 words that you wish to be used by others to describe your character.

"Choose to show your best character every day and watch how far you will go above and beyond."
—Gayle Woodard

Notes

Notes

*"Do not compromise your standards.
No one is worth more than you."*

—Doris Randle

How Does Your Character Shine?

"Whoever walks in integrity walks securely, but he who makes his ways crooked will be found out."

Proverbs 10:9

How do you define character?

_____
_____
_____
_____
_____

How do others describe your character?

_____
_____
_____
_____
_____

How do you describe your own character?

_____
_____
_____
_____
_____

What do you believe God would say about your character and does it please Him?

_____

_____

_____

_____

_____

What character traits can you improve?

_____

_____

_____

_____

_____

"Beauty begins the moment
you decide to be yourself."
—Coco Chanel

Do You Treat Your Body as a Temple?

**"Or do you not know that your body is a temple of
the Holy Spirit within you, whom you have from God?
You are not your own."**
1 Corinthians 6:19

Do you honor God with your body?

_____

_____

_____

_____

_____

Since you know your body is not your own, how would you guard it?

_____

_____

_____

_____

_____

What changes will you make to honor God with your body in the
future?

_____

_____

_____

_____

_____

Are you willing to submit to the Holy Spirit and allow Him to help you make these changes?

_____

_____

_____

_____

_____

"Get up! Dress up! It is not based on how you feel. It is based on how you look and where you are going. Make it happen."
—Gayle Woodard

Embrace
Your Best You

A woman's attitude in life has the power to influence her perception and her perception has the power to influence her mark on the world.

"The greatest discovery of all time is that a person can change his future by merely changing his attitude."
-Oprah Winfrey

A woman's class is her decision to hold herself to high standards and to help others do the same in a kind and respectful way.

"When they go low, we go high."
-Michelle Obama

A woman's determination is what keeps her moving closer to her best self even when she is the only one who believes she can.

"I never gave up even though others told me I wouldn't make it. I saw the bigger picture and I went after it."
-Taraji P. Henson

Notes

Notes

Notes

Do Your Words Speak Life or Death?

"Death and life are in the power of the tongue,
and those who love it will eat its fruits."
Proverbs 18:21

What is your tone when you speak to others?

_____
_____
_____
_____
_____

What is your motive when you speak about others?

_____
_____
_____
_____
_____

Do you speak life or death to yourself?

_____
_____
_____
_____
_____

In what ways do you speak God's word in your daily atmosphere?

_____

_____

_____

_____

_____

Even in difficult situations, how can you speak in a loving and peaceful way?

_____

_____

_____

_____

_____

"Fight for things that you care about but do it in a way that will lead others to join you."
—Ruth Bader Ginsburg

Do You Use Your Power of Wisdom?

**"One who is wise is cautious and turns away from evil,
but a fool is reckless and careless."**
Proverbs 14:16

How do you practice wisdom?

_____
_____
_____
_____
_____

In what ways have you chosen wisdom over ignorance, fear, or pride?

_____
_____
_____
_____
_____

Name a time when it was uncomfortable to make a wise decision?

_____
_____
_____
_____
_____

How do you respond to constructive criticism from others? How do you control your emotions as a wise woman?

_____

_____

_____

_____

_____

"Jealousy is a joke; don't allow it to make you feel insecure. That is not your best."

—Gayle Woodard

Became Your Best You in Relationships

ACTIVITY

Discuss with your group different relationships that can benefit from the positive actions below:

Be sensitive to your differences

Communicate with a desire to understand

Be patient in stages

Bravely communicate your thoughts and feelings

Hold on to mercy and release unforgiveness

Notes

Notes

"Make decisions based on hope and possibility. Make decision based on what should happen, not what shouldn't."

—Michelle Obama

What Are You Committed to First?

"You shall love the Lord your God with all your heart and with all your soul and with all your might."
Deuteronomy 6:5

How do you prioritize your relationships?

_____

_____

_____

_____

_____

What ways do you spend time getting to know God?

_____

_____

_____

_____

_____

What are three commitments you have made to God?

_____

_____

_____

_____

_____

In what ways can you keep and improve those commitments to Him?

_____

_____

_____

_____

_____

What are somethings that has challenged your commitment to God?

_____

_____

_____

_____

_____

**"I have stood on a mountain of
no's for one yes."**
—B. Smith

Are You Leading by Example?

**"Older women likewise are to be reverent
in behavior, not slanders or slaves too much wine.
They are to teach what is good."**
Titus 2:3-4

Who has encouraged you to be a better person?

_____

_____

_____

_____

_____

Who have you encouraged to be a better person?

_____

_____

_____

_____

_____

How do you lead by example?

_____

_____

_____

_____

_____

How does your advice to others match up with your actions?

_____

_____

_____

_____

_____

What is a piece of advice you given in the past that you wish you had listened to?

_____

_____

_____

_____

_____

"Step out of your comfort zone and make a statement to make a difference."

—Gayle Woodard

Do You Believe?

"If you can believe, all things
are possible to him who believes."
Mark 9:23

When you read the word of God, why do you trust that it works?

_____

_____

_____

_____

_____

How have you experienced having to believe in God without
understanding what he allowed?

_____

_____

_____

_____

_____

How has your faith encouraged others to believe?

_____

_____

_____

_____

_____

How has your belief in God been challenged?

_____

_____

_____

_____

_____

When you pray, do you believe that your prayers are answered?

_____

_____

_____

_____

_____

"Bring your best to the moment. Then, whether it fails or succeeds, at least you know you gave it all you had. We need to live the best that's in us."
—Angela Bassett

Reaching Your Goals

**"Commit your work to the Lord, and
your plans will be established."
Proverbs 16:3**

To become your best you, you must have goals and a vision for your future!

Long Term Goal (3 years to 5 years):

_____

_____

_____

_____

_____

Date to Accomplish:

_____

Steps to Prioritize:
1.
2.
3.

Short Term Goal (6 months to 1 year):

_____

_____

_____

_____

_____

Date to Accomplish:

_____

Steps to Prioritize:
1.
2.
3.

Be Your Best You and "Just Do It"

No one can believe in you better than you can do it.

No one can see your vision better than you can see it.

No one can act out your gift better than you can do it.

No one can activate your blessings better than you can do it.

No one can be you better than you.

"Do all things to the best of your ability because that's your excellence."
—Gayle Woodard

Notes

Notes

Notes

Five Steps to Becoming Your Best You

1. Do not forget where you come from.

2. Be authentic and grateful in who God created you to be.

3. Find how your purpose connects to who you are.

4. Do what brings you joy, excitement and motivation.

5. When you fall, persevere, and get back up.

That is becoming your best you!

"Just because you are successful doesn't mean you have arrived, stay humble and grateful."
—Gayle Woodard

"Owning our story can be hard, but not nearly as difficult as spending our lives running from it."

—Brené Brown

Renewing Your Best Mind, Body & Soul

ACTIVITY

Discuss with your group different ways you can each make a commitment to incorporate a few of these actions in your everyday life to help renew your mind, body, and soul.

Mind
Meditate
Study the word of God

Body
Exercise
Eat healthy foods

Soul
Pray
Set aside time for worship

ACTIVITY

Tic–Tac Toe Improvements

Play with a friend and decide who will represent X and who will represent O.

After choosing each space, discuss with your friend how you will improve that topic in your life.

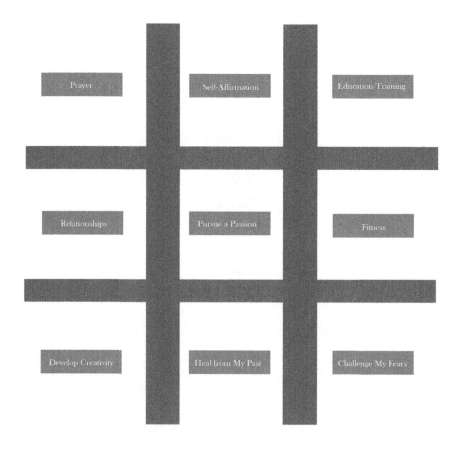

ACTIVITY

A Maze to Success

Trace the lines in the maze to link each step and discuss with your group how you can find your way to success based on these steps.

Notes

Notes

Notes

Notes

"The most alluring thing a woman can have is confidence."

—Beyoncé Knowles-Carter

Be Your Best You Despite the Circumstances

Moment of Inspiration

The inspiring story of Esther in the Bible. Read the empowering story in the book of Esther.

Esther's Childhood

Esther's mother & father died, and she did not have the mother/daughter bond and guidance as a young woman. Although she had a tragic past, she did not let her past dictate her destiny.

Is there anything you did not receive as a child that affected your confidence in your ability to succeed?

_____

_____

_____

_____

_____

_____

_____

_____

_____

_____

Esther was a Jewish girl

Esther's cousin knew that Esther had to wait to reveal her Jewish identity because she would not be given the same opportunity to be queen as the other women who were presented. The King of Persia ruled over the Jewish people and the King's advisor, Haman planned to kill Jewish people.

Have you ever met someone who treated you with a lack of respect based on where you came from or what you did not have?

_____
_____
_____
_____
_____
_____
_____
_____
_____
_____

Esther's Competition

There were many women who wanted to be the Queen and who were Persian, beautiful and talented. Esther's true inner beauty and spirit shined even brighter than her outer beauty.

Have you ever compared your beauty, intelligence, success, or blessings with someone else's? If so, why?

_____

_____

_____

_____

_____

_____

_____

_____

_____

_____

Esther's Faith Was Challenged

Esther depended on her faith and used the tools she was given
to fast and pray in agreement with other servants of God. She
was willing to risk her life to be an example of what she
believed in.

Give an example of a time that you chose your faith in the
presence of your fear?

_____

_____

_____

_____

_____

_____

_____

_____

_____

Notes

Be Your Best You While Moving Forward

Moment of Inspiration

The inspiring story of Rehab in the Bible. Read the empowering story in the book of Joshua, Chapter 2.

Rehab's Background & Sacrifice

Rehab made a lot of poor choices in life and she wore the labels of failure. Although she made mistakes, God never gives up on his children and those who honor Him in their actions. One day Joshua and the Israelites were about to attack the city of Jericho where Rehab lived. Two men were sent out to spy out the land and word got to the king that spies had entered the city. Now the two spies were in great danger. Out of all the people God could have used to protect the spies, God chose Rehab. Risking her own life, Rehab took the men into her home and hid them. Rahab saved their lives and the two spies said to Rehab "we're going to wipe out the whole city but because you honored God by showing us favor we will spare you and anyone in this home." When the city of Jericho was conquered, Rahab and her family were the only ones saved.

Moving forward, what sacrifices will you make to save your life?

_____

_____

_____

_____

_____

_____

_____

_____

_____

_____

_____

Rehab's Future & Grace

In the mist of bad life choices, you still have the opportunity to make one choice towards becoming your best you. Rehab was a woman in the Bible who was a prostitute and despite her choice to devalue herself, she became a heroine to the people of God by her choice to be the best version of herself. Rehab help create a legacy that led to Jesus Christ.

How will you allow your present choices to determine your future?

_____

_____

_____

_____

_____

_____

_____

_____

_____

_____

Fear Attracts Mediocrity

Recognize Your Fear

The presence of fear is normal, but the acceptance of fear can lead to the acceptance of unfulfillment.

Confront Your Fear

Think of your greatest fears and expose them as your unguided thoughts and not your truth.

Dismantle Your fear

Fears do not provide opportunities, fears steal opportunities.

Fight Your Fear

Dare to challenge your thoughts of fear by remembering your capabilities.

Recite the scripture 2 Timothy 1:7

"For God gave us a spirit not of fear but of power and love and self-control."

Fear Rejects Greatness

Recognize Your Fear
Fear can help you to seek safety, but fear can not help you to seek your best you.

Confront Your Fear
Think of your greatest accomplishment and expose the times that you ignored your fears of failing.

Dismantle Your fear
Every person who operates in greatness knows that fear has no power without permission.

Fight Your Fear
Dare to praise God for deliverance from fear while the fear is present.

Recite the scripture Joshua 1:9
"Have I not commanded you? Be strong and courageous. Do not be frightened, and do not be dismayed, for the LORD your God is with you wherever you go."

Faith Rejects Mediocrity

Recognize Your Faith

The presence of a small amount of faith in your mind is proof that you know better is possible.

Build Your Faith

Decide on 3 areas of your life that you lack faith in and read a scripture pertaining to each area daily.

Reveal Your Faith

Share with a friend something that you are believing God to improve in your life.

Stand on Your Faith

Have confidence that God has equipped you to strive for more and not to settle for less.

Recite the scripture Hebrews 11:6

"And without faith it is impossible to please him, for whoever would draw near to God must believe that he exists and that he rewards those who seek him."

Faith Attracts Greatness

Recognize Your Faith

Faith is the fuel that will allow you to reach your destination to your best you.

Build Your Faith

In a daily prayer, thank God for the greatness you will achieve in a specific area of your life this year.

Reveal Your Faith

Find a mentor who has achieved great things and request for them to pray with you.

Stand Your Faith

Achievement requires consistency in both times when you do and when you do not see your greatness.

Recite the scripture Philippians 4:13

"I can do all things through him who strengthens me."

Pledge to be Your Best You

I _____ (full name), am fearfully
and wonderfully made in the image of an all mighty God.
I am unique and different from anyone else. God created me
to be one of a kind. I carry beauty on the inside of me and I
allow it to shine on the outside of me. I am a woman of
purpose who has goals and aspirations. I am a Christian,
classy and confident woman. My expectations are high
because I know what I am capable of and I trust God to lead
me in what I may not know that I am capable of. I am a
delicate, but strong and gentle woman who holds great
power. Now I pledge to be my best.

Becoming Your Best You

JOURNAL

Notes

Notes

Notes

Notes

Notes

Notes

Notes

Notes

Notes

Notes

Notes

Notes

Notes

Notes

Notes

Notes

Notes

Notes

Notes

Notes

Notes

Notes

Notes

Notes

Notes

Notes

Notes

Notes

Notes

Notes

Notes

Notes

Made in the USA
Middletown, DE
24 September 2021

48177261R00060